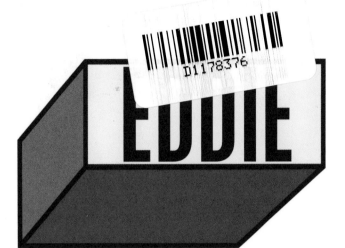

EDDIE WOO'S MAGICAL MATHS

EDDIE WOO'S MAGICAL MATHS

Macmillan
Pan Macmillan Australia

First published 2019 in Macmillan by Pan Macmillan Australia Pty Ltd
1 Market Street, Sydney, New South Wales, Australia, 2000

Cataloguing-in-Publication entry is available
from the National Library of Australia
http://catalogue.nla.gov.au

Cover and text design by Alissa Dinallo
Illustrations by Alissa Dinallo
Images on pages 50, 51, 84, 87, 88, 96, 108, 110, 111, 115, 116, 148
and 166 courtesy of Shutterstock.

Printed in China by Hang Tai Printing Co. Ltd

CONTENTS

THE NUMBER FILES   01

SHAPING UP   32

BRANCHING INTO FRACTALS   78

THE INSIDE STORY   160

MATHEMAGIC   176

ENDING ON A RAINBOW   182

ANSWERS   190

ALL ABOUT EDDIE

8

6

2

Eddie Woo is the head mathematics teacher at Cherrybrook Technology High School, Sydney. He has been teaching mathematics for more than ten years.

In 2012, Eddie started recording his lessons and uploading them to YouTube – creating 'Wootube'. Since then, he has amassed a following of more than 600,000 subscribers and his videos have been viewed more than 34 million times.

In 2018, Eddie was named Australia's Local Hero of the Year and shortlisted as one of the top ten teachers in the world.

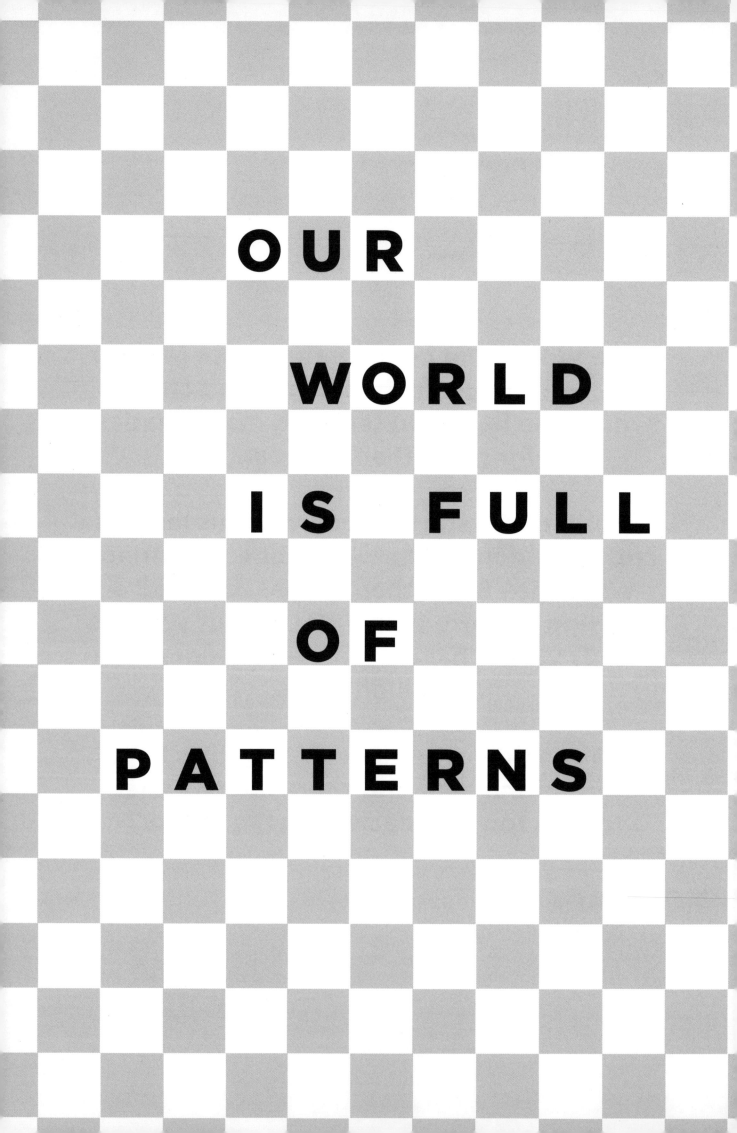

OUR WORLD IS FULL OF PATTERNS

A NOTE TO THE READER

This book was made for you to have **FUN** and learn amazing things about the wonders and magic of maths.

Feel free to scribble and make notes all over the pages.

There are plenty of fun activities to do. Look out for the activity symbols throughout:

You'll find all the answers to these activities in a TOP SECRET section at the back of the book.
DO NOT PEEK.

Most importantly, don't forget to
ENJOY MATHS!

THIS WAY TO BEGIN YOUR

MATHS ADVENTURE

Numbers make the world go round.

THE NUM

BER FILES

They are inside and outside you and me and everyone.

NUMBER ME

MY NUMBER PROFILE:

Full name ___Eddie Woo___

My birthday is ___19 September___.

I have ___1___ sister(s).

I have ___1___ brother(s).

I have ___3___ children.

I have written ___2___ books.

I have ___0___ pets.

Q: Why was 6 afraid of 7?

NUMBER YOU

YOUR NUMBER PROFILE:

PASTE YOUR PHOTO HERE

Full name _Jayden Basst_

I am _10_ years old.

My birthday is _1st augest_

My best friend is _11_ years old.

I have _1_ sister(s).

I have _0_ brother(s).

I have _2_ eyes.

I have _2_ legs.

I have _2_ arms.

I have _1_ heart.

I have _2_ kidneys.

I have _1_ liver.

There are _32?_ kids in my class.

My lucky number is _7_.

I know _10_ times tables off by heart.

I know _haiku_ poems.

I have _0_ pets.

I have _0?_ freckles.

I know _lots of_ jokes.

This is my favourite joke:

knock Rhock
wks there
dWane

dwane who
dwane the
bathtub i'm
dwowning

A: Because 7 8 9!

3

16

8

45

76

47

Odd numbers are numbers that can't be split into two equal groups of whole numbers.

77

83

31

56

82

34

2

99

12

74

1

73

44

84

HOW

51

60

57

3

5

38

37

85

81

7

25

13

33

68

66

48

40

4

79

55

6

94

26

30

9

75

43

95

58

65

22

15

39

24

90

61

91

64

BUT a pair of odd numbers
always adds up to an
even number.

52

80

71

21

97

50

36

19

67

62

88

28

54

29

11

46

41

32

87

89

63

98

49

27

23

72

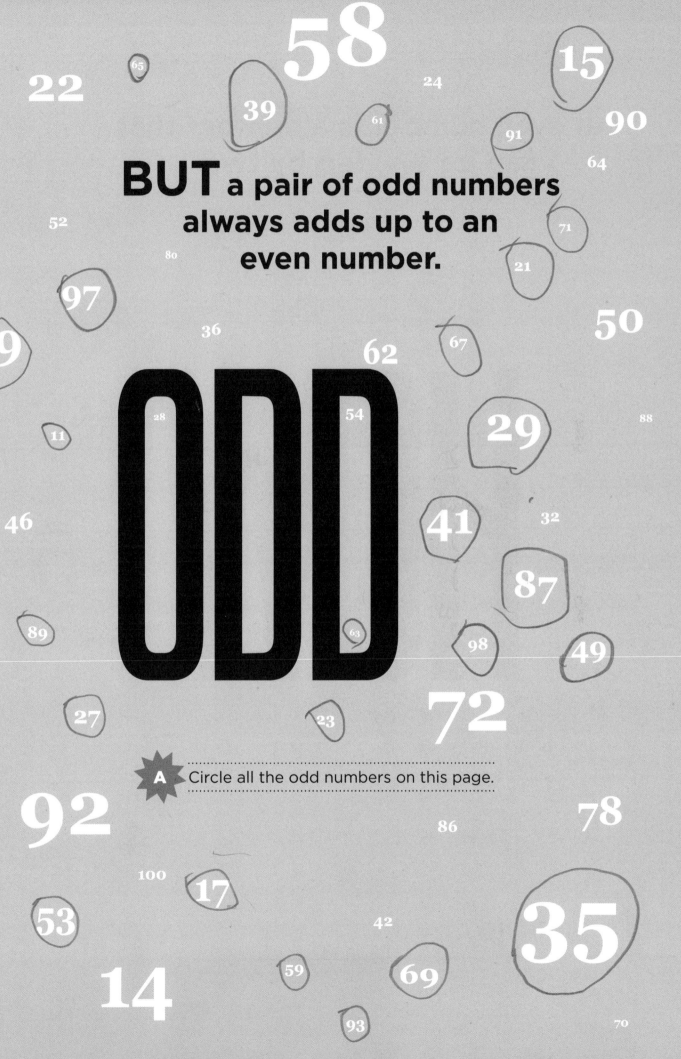

A Circle all the odd numbers on this page.

92

86

78

100

17

53

42

35

14

59

69

93

70

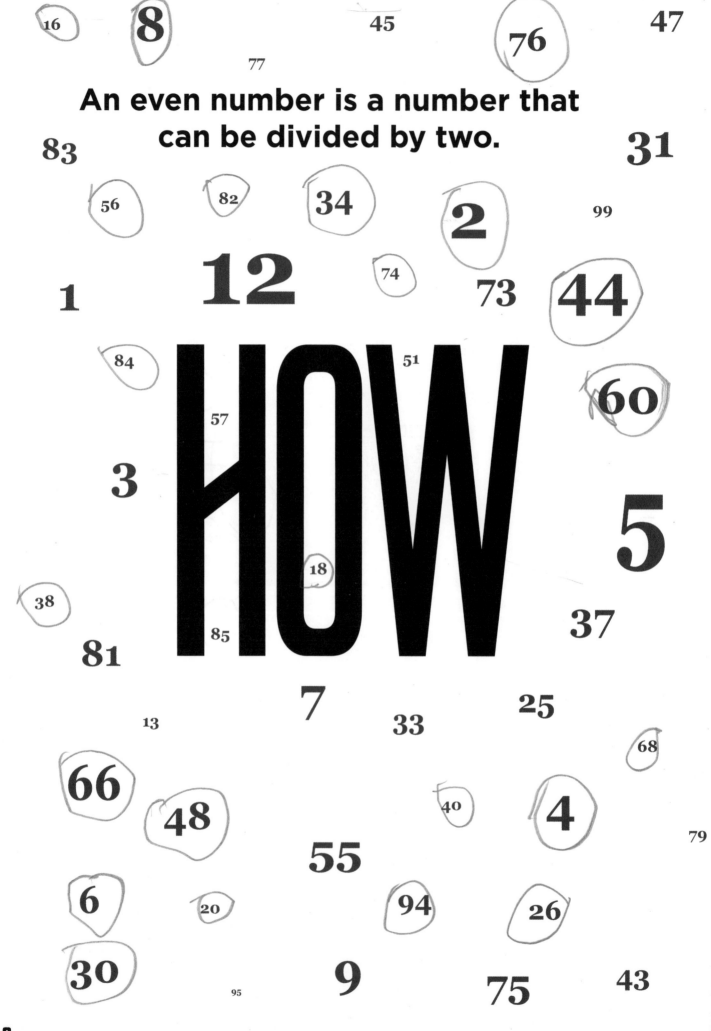

An even number is a number that can be divided by two.

58

15

22   65   24   90

39   61   91   64

52   71

80   21

97   50

19   36   96   62   67   29   88

EVEN

28   54   32   41

11   87

46   49

98   63

89

27   23   72

A Circle all the even numbers on this page.

92   86   78

100   17

53   42   35

14   59   69

93   70

ODDS GET EVEN

A Turn all these odd numbers into even numbers as *fast* as you can.

1 + 3 = __4__

3 + 5 = __8__

5 + 7 = __12__

7 + 9 = __16__

9 + 11 = __20__

11 + 13 = __24__

13 + 15 = __28__

15 + 17 = _____

17 + 19 = _____

19 + 21 = _____

21 + 23 = _____

23 + 25 = _____

25 + 27 = _____

27 + 29 = _____

Q: How do you make seven an even number?

A Draw your starting and finishing times.

READY, SET, GO!

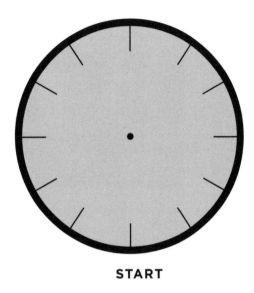

START

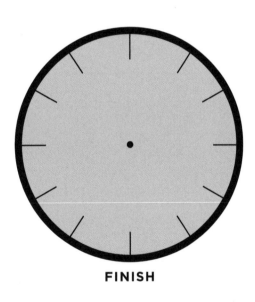

FINISH

RECORD BOX

BEAT YOURSELF
I added them up in _____ minutes.

BEAT YOUR FRIEND
_____ added them up in _____ minutes.

BEAT ME
Eddie added them up in ___2___ minutes.

A: Just remove the 's'!

PRIMA

Three is an odd number.

3

3

Hey, who are you calling *ODD?*

THREE

There are 3 sides to a triangle.

There are **3** building blocks of atoms: the proton, the neutron and the electron.

There are **3** main kinds of matter: gaseous, *liquid* and **SOLID**.

There are **3** main kinds of big objects: **PLANETS, STARS AND GALAXIES.**

There are **3** main kinds of galaxies: spiral galaxies, irregular galaxies and elliptical galaxies.

DONNA

Good things come in threes

YAY

Bad things come in threes

NAY

2 is one of my favourite numbers.

THE POWER OF
TWO
TWO

Can you guess WHY?

Take the True or False test to find out.

2 is one of my favourite numbers because:

	TRUE	FALSE
1. It's **1** more than **1**?	☑	☐
2. It rhymes with **WOO**?	☑	☐
3. **EDDIE** has **2** syllables?	☑	☐
4. I have **2** feet.	☑	☐
5. It takes me **2** minutes to eat a bar of chocolate.	☐ ?	☐
6. Double trouble means **TROUBLE** x 2.	☐	☒

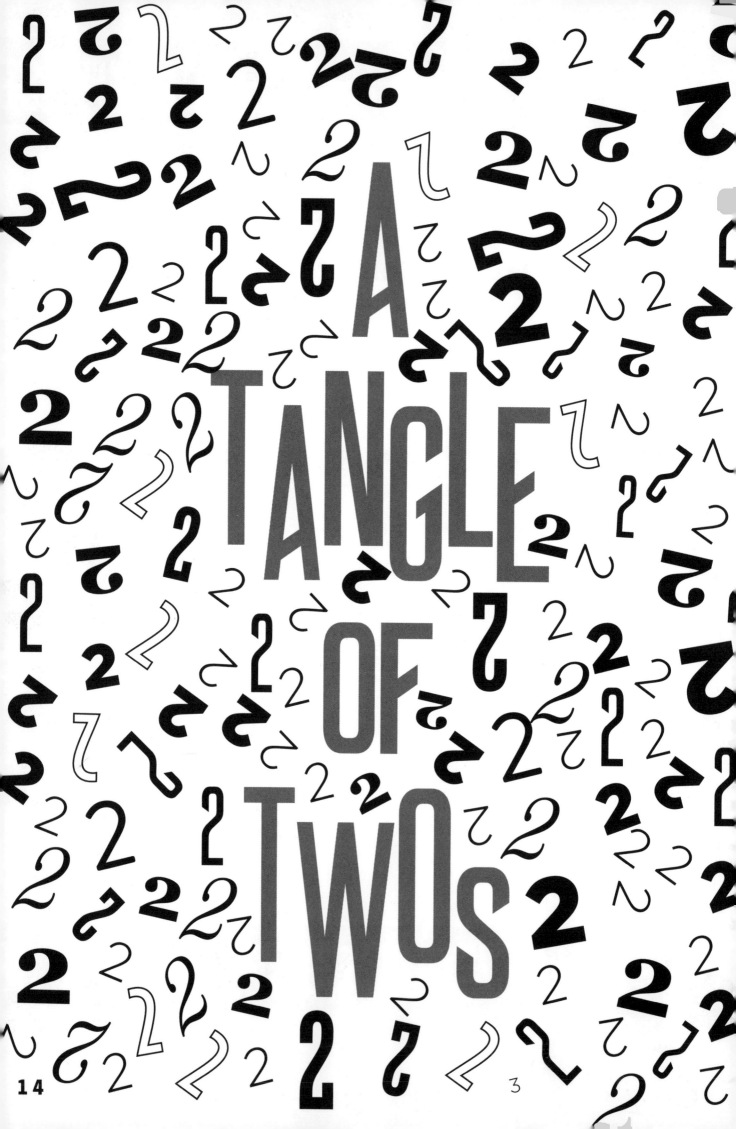

A TANGLE OF TWOS

A poem for two (that's me and you).

Write a poem using as many words as you can that rhyme with two.

Here are just a few suggestions for you:

blue

shoe

moo

flu

Sue

blew

chew

ewe

dew

few

grew

queue

spew → use sparingly

true → use lavishly

who

WOO → that's me!

YOU → that's you!

MY TWO-RRIFIC POEM

Written by: _____

_____

_____

_____

_____

_____

_____

_____

_____

_____

_____

_____

_____

_____

_____

The End

FUN WITH
FIBONACCI

0, 1, 1, 2, 3, 5, 8, 13, 21, 34

Look closely at this pattern of numbers.

Can you work out the next six numbers?

No peeking at
the answers
upside down
on the next
page.

YES, I CAN :)

They are

WOW! YOU ARE A SUPER MATHS SLEUTH

NO, I CAN'T :(

Can I have a clue, please?

CLUE FOR YOU: You can find the next number in the sequence by adding up the two numbers that come before it.

This is called the
FIBONACCI SEQUENCE
because it was discovered by an Italian mathematician called LEONARDO BONACCI.

WOO NUMBERS

The Woo numbers start off with a 19 and a 9, because my birthday is 19 September. After that, you get the next number in the sequence by adding two adjacent numbers - just like you did to get the next number in the Fibonacci sequence.

Here is the beginning of the list of Woo Numbers:

19, 9, 28, 37, 65, 102, 167, 269, 436, 705, 1141, 1846, 2987, 4833 . . .

YOU NUMBERS

Your numbers should begin with your birthday:
the day and then the month. Then you can work out
the next number, the next number, the next number
and so on and so on until you want to stop.

OR your head **EXPLODES** with so many numbers inside it.

_____

_____

_____

SUNFLOWER SECRET

Many patterns in nature reflect the Fibonacci sequence.

Sunflowers, for example, are hiding a very special pattern. If you look closely at the seeds in the middle of a sunflower, you'll see that they seem to form spiral patterns that curve left and right.

If you count these spirals, your total will be a Fibonacci number.

HAPPY FIBONACCI DAY

Fibonacci Day is celebrated on November 23 because this date has the digits **1 1 2 3**, which is part of the Fibonacci sequence.

One of these sunflowers is not like the others.
Can you spot which one?

Colour in all the sunflowers to
make this page pop.

LITTLE BOXES

Fibonacci wasn't the only one who had a fascination with number patterns.

ÉDOUARD LUCAS was a 19th-century French mathematician. He also invented one of my favourite maths games:

BOXES.

Play with a friend to see who can join the dots to form the most boxes. Whoever joins up the 4th side should write his or her initial in the box and draw another line.

PLAYER A = ━━━   **PLAYER B =** • • • • • • •

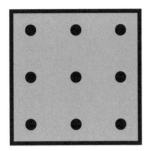 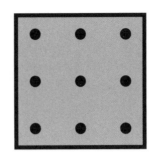 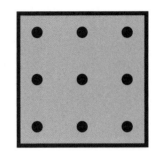

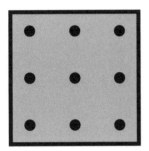 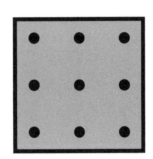 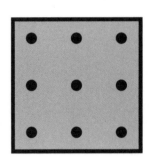

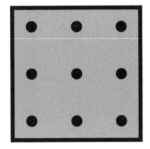 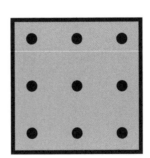 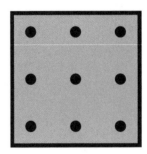

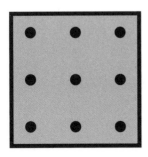 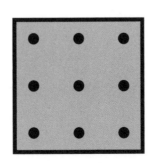 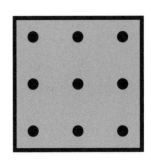

MORE LITTLE BOXES

PLAYER A = ——— **PLAYER B =** • • • • • • •

MORE LITTLE BOXES

PLAYER A = ——   **PLAYER B =** ·······

THE GAME OF
23

You need two players.

PLAYER 1 chooses a number from 1 to 4.

For example: **2**

PLAYER 2 adds a number from 1 to 4 with
PLAYER 1'S number.

For example: **2 + 3 = 5**

PLAYER 1 adds a number from 1 to 4.

For example: **5 + 1 = 6**

Keep taking turns until one person adds a number to equal

23.

THEY ARE THE *WINNER!*

Brought to you by ...

SOME OF YOUR
FAVOURITE
SHAPES!

SHAPING

A Use a RED pencil or texta to colour in all the triangles with a '1' inside them.

A Colour in the rest of the triangles with as many colours (other than red) as possible.

SQUARE

A 3D square is called a cube.

A

SPOT THE SQUARE:
Look around your neighbourhood.
What can you see that's square?
Write your answers in the squares above.

SQUARE FACTS

I have four equal sides.

I have four right angles.

Squares are everywhere.

Q: What kind of snake is good at maths?

Play noughts and crosses in these squares.

A: An Adder!

How to

DRAW 3D

A cube

1. Draw a square.

2. Draw a second square to the top right of the first square.

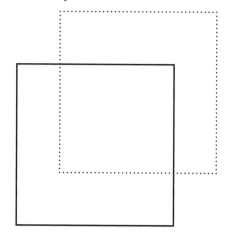

3. Connect each corner of the square with straight lines.

4. *VOILA!*

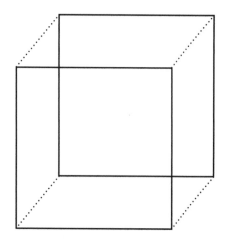

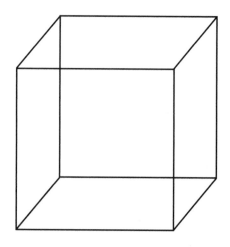

A cone

1. Draw an oval.

2. Draw a point some-where above the oval.

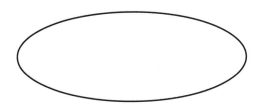

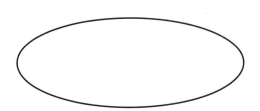

3. Draw two straight lines that connect the dot to the outer edges of the oval.

4. *VOILA!*

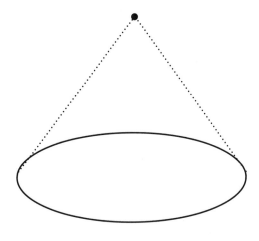

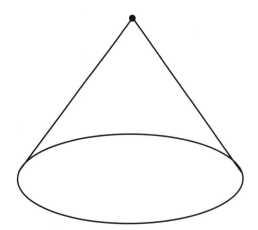

A Use these pages to practise drawing 3D shapes like these.

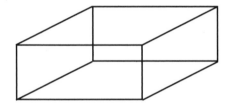

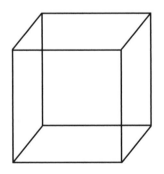

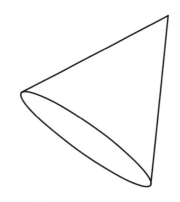

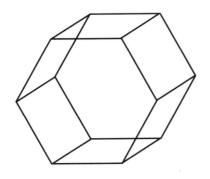

CIRCLE

CIRCLE FACTS

The diameter of a circle is the straight line from one side to the other.

The circumference of a circle is the distance around the outside.

SCRAMBLED CIRCLES

 Unscramble these circular foods. Then write your answers in the circles from your favourite to your least favourite food.

esip

kaepsacn

uhdsuotgn

zipazs

llmaebats

ishus

grbures

ssnoce

upkaccse

GOING ROUND IN CIRCLES

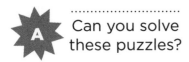 Can you solve these puzzles?

Hint: They're all circle sayings.

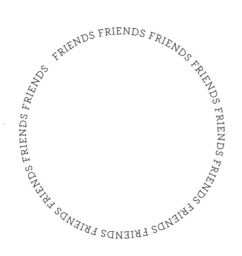

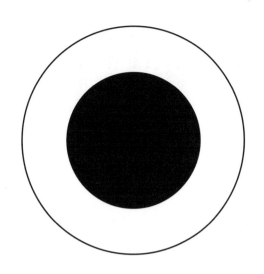

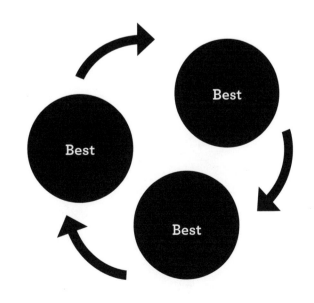

TRIANGLE

A WIZARD'S HAT

A How many things do you know that are in the shape of a triangle? Write your answers in the triangles above.

Hint: I've done one for you.

RECTANGLE

I am right from every angle.

How many things do you know that are in the shape of a rectangle? Write your answers in the rectangles above.

Hint: you are looking at one right now.

Hexagon

AS BUSY AS A

Bees build **hexagonal** honeycombs. They live and work in these honeycombs, storing honey and raising little bees.

Hexagons are COMPACT and *efficient* shapes. They are easy for the bees to build and this means they can use their energy on other things such as making honey.

Q: What do you call a clumsy bee?

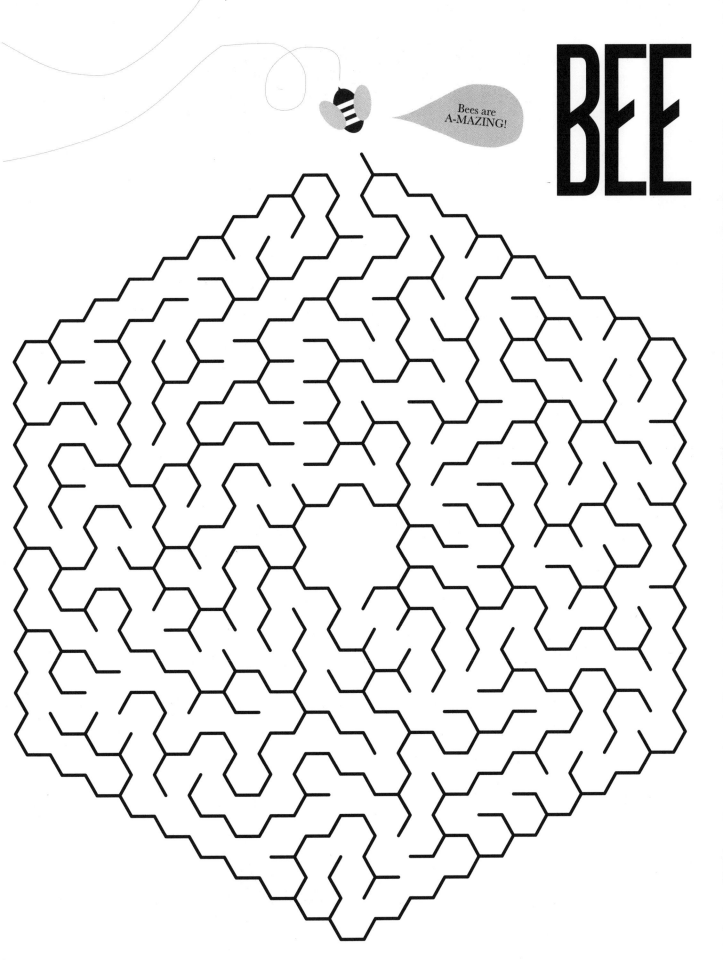

BEE

Bees are A-MAZING!

Help Mr Buzz find his way to the centre of his beehive.

A: A bumblebee.

A SPELLING BEE

This little bee has some serious spelling to do.
Test yourself with a friend (or two). To make it more tricky,
though, you need to work out what some of the words are
first before you can spell them.

EASY PEASY WORDS

I rhyme with bone and I ring. I am a _____

I start with 't' and am not today or yesterday.

I am _____

I have hands but I can't clap with them. I am a _____

UNSCRAMBLE ME

glrafie

butoncriinto

efrontu

EVEN LESS EASY WORDS

accommodation

collaboration

borborygmus

I am a rumbling in your tummy.
I can be very loud.

PENTAGON

PENTA MEANS FIVE!

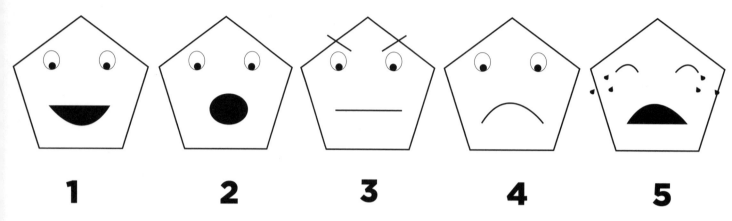

1   2   3   4   5

TRAPEZIUM

OCTAGON

OCTO MEANS EIGHT!

HIDDEN HEX

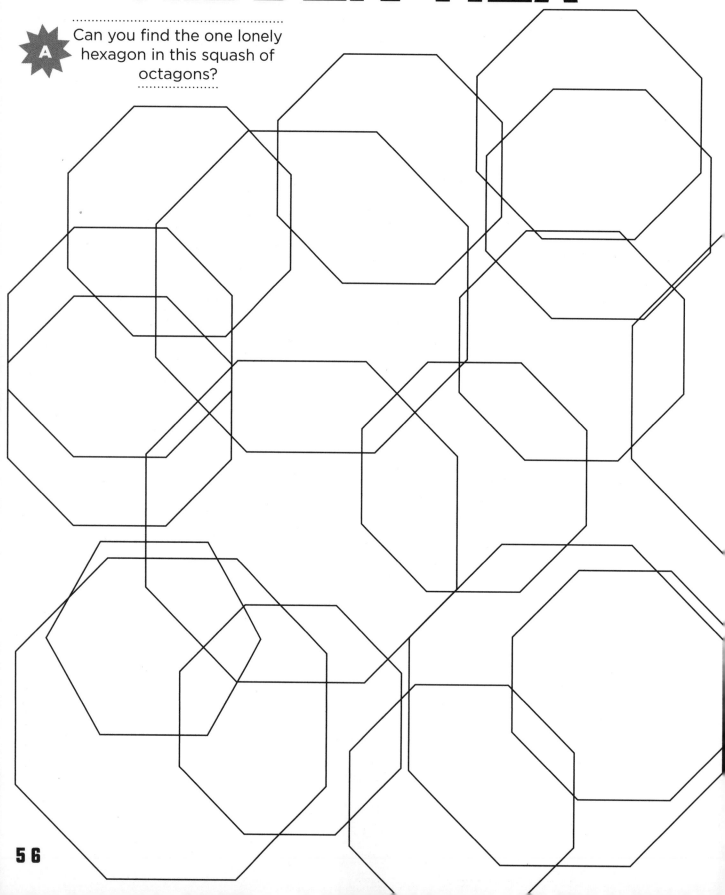

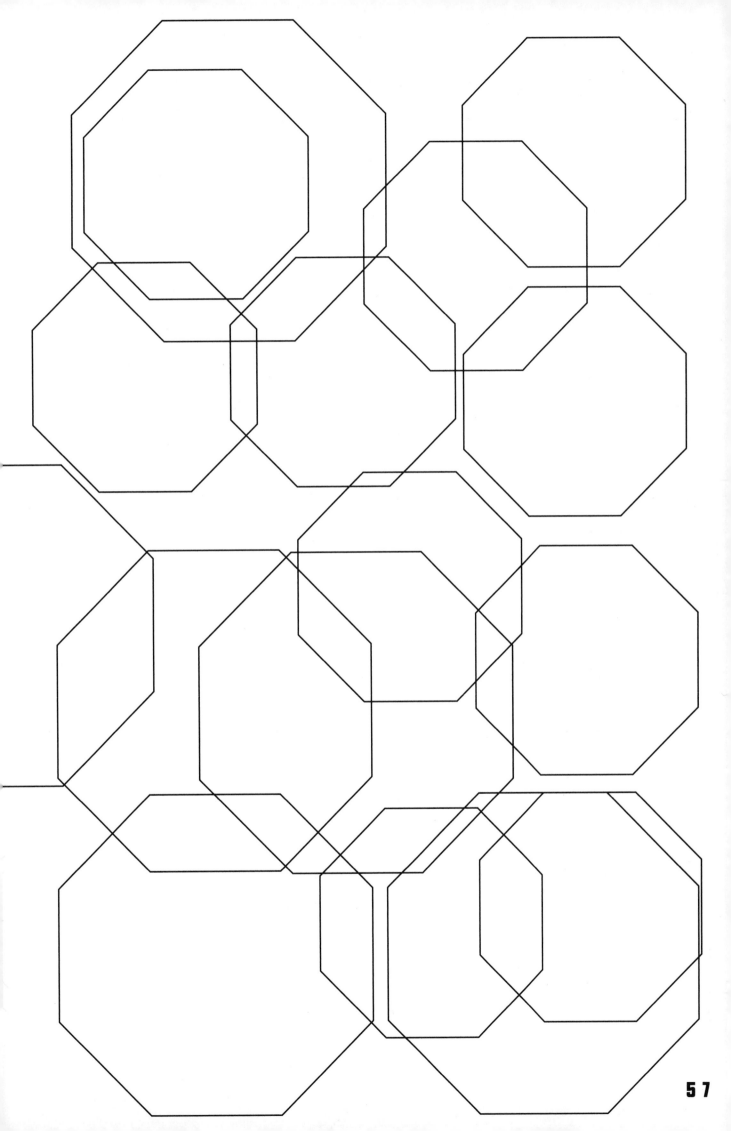

57

OCTO SEARCH

Find these five OCTO words in the word search below:

octopus   octonauts   doctor

octogenerian   October

```
K  F  D  B  G  X  T  M  J  R  U  S  H  X  B  M
V  L  O  S  W  C  B  G  J  X  K  N  O  N  P  Y
A  W  M  G  T  H  F  A  B  P  L  B  C  S  I  F
H  L  R  Z  A  K  R  I  Q  N  I  S  T  G  D  Y
V  S  A  R  Y  G  I  M  J  O  R  A  O  K  U  E
I  E  O  C  T  O  P  U  S  C  V  Q  N  W  F  W
W  L  Z  D  R  Z  C  D  U  P  D  S  A  P  J  I
Y  A  W  T  J  L  W  M  V  N  K  B  U  X  C  M
N  G  H  C  L  U  X  P  H  G  F  O  T  Q  M  L
K  V  I  J  N  A  Z  R  E  C  D  Z  S  E  K  R
U  H  X  M  B  P  O  Q  C  L  Y  K  T  O  N  E
D  W  E  V  O  T  J  U  Q  A  D  H  H  V  Z  B
J  B  L  F  C  E  Z  K  Y  O  R  F  O  P  N  O
T  I  Q  O  S  T  D  T  S  J  Y  X  M  D  T  T
Z  V  D  H  C  U  Q  O  N  B  U  H  P  I  Y  C
Q  S  O  C  T  O  G  E  N  E  R  I  A  N  T  O
```

BEWARE!

TURN THIS PAGE WITH CAUTION.

Especially if you're an

ARACHNOPHOBE.

If you don't know what this means, grab a dictionary and find out.

BEFORE IT'S TOO LATE!

SHOCK OF A

SPIDERS

Too many!

I hope I never have to use this equation!

How many spiders' legs are on this cobweb?

Write your answer as an equation:

___ spiders × 8 legs = ___ spiders' legs.

A

61

MEMORY GAME

Can you name each shape?
Check the answers on page 206
and add up your score.

_____

_____

_____

_____

_____

_____

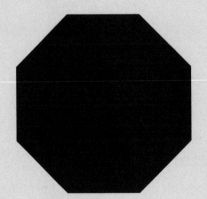

_____

_____

HOW DID YOU SCORE
IN THE MEMORY GAME?

8 OUT OF 8: Excellent. You are on top of the world of shapes.

5-7: Well done. You are very close to excellence (some closer than others). Keep going. Reach for the stars.

4-6 : You are middling in the middle.
The only way is UP⬆

3-5: Hmm. Shape up or shape out!

1-3: Don't despair. You can only get better (because you really can't get much worse).

MY SHAPE SCORE IS:

/ 8

THE SHAPE OF YOU

**If you were a shape,
what would you be?**

_____

_____

_____

Draw yourself as a shape with arms and legs.

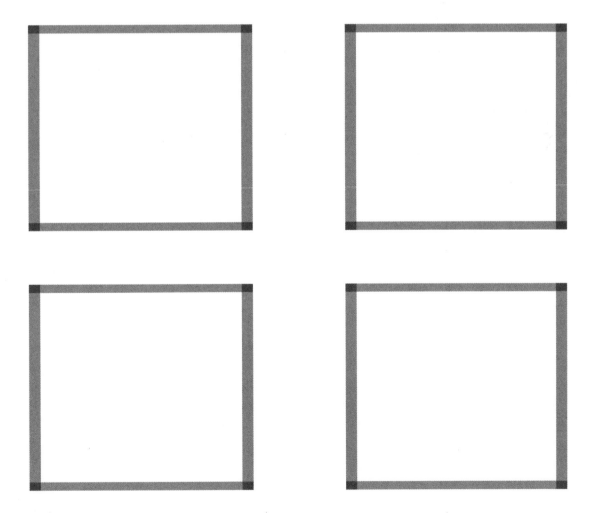

 In the frames above, draw the members of your family as shapes.

✦ JOINING THE DOTS

1. Place four dots anywhere on the page.

2. Connect the dots with a ruler.

(Don't put your pen down yet! This activity continues on page 70)

CONGRATULATIONS!

Take a bow.
Take a holiday.
Take an extra dollop of
ice-cream at dinner.

You are the proud creator of
a four-sided **POLYGON**.

This four-sided polygon
is also known as a

QUADRILATERAL.

Your quadrilateral on page 68 looks like every other quadrilateral *BUT*

3. Using your ruler again, find the point that is exactly in the middle of each side.

4. You have four sides so you will have four points.

5. Now, join them up.

The shape you're looking at in the middle of your irregular quadrilateral is a perfect **PARALLELOGRAM**.

The sides that are **opposite** to each other are **exactly the same length**. And they are **precisely parallel** – pointing in the same direction.

You can extend them forever in both directions and they will **never EVER** meet.

QUAD MEANS FOUR

QUAD-MATCH

 Connect these five QUAD words with their correct meanings:

quadrangle

four siblings

quadrillion

a square or rectangular space
surrounded by buildings

quadruped

a really **large** number

quadruplets

walks on **four** feet

quadrille

a square dance performed by four couples

FLASH FACT:
*Spinosaurus
aegyptiacus
was a
quadruped.*

SHAPE

Mathematicians who specialise in shapes are called GEOmeters.

I see shapes!

A Greek called Euclid was the great-great-great grandfather of all geometers.

SHIFTERS

Q. Can you name all the shapes that make up Euclid's face?

WHO DOES WHAT?

Match the professions with their descriptions:

A biologist	studies substances
A physicist	studies slugs
A chemist	studies stars and planets
A garbologist	studies rocks
An astronomer	studies living things
A geologist	studies moving things
A mathematician	studies fish
An ichthyologist	studies garbage
A limacologist	studies patterns

HOW GREAT IS THAT?

Who was your great-great-great grandfather?

Find out ALL you can about him.

MY GREAT-GREAT-GREAT GRANDPA

Name: _____

Nickname: _____

Born: _____

Died: _____

Occupation: _____

Favourite games: _____

Favourite food: _____

Favourite word: _____

Favourite anything else: _____

_____

Draw a picture of him – maybe using an
old photo as reference.

BRANCHING

INTO

FRACTALS

NATURE

IS

FULL OF PATTERNS

GETTING BACK TO NATURE

There are many amazing, never-ending patterns in nature.

They form the structure of things like:

lightning

snowflakes

frost crystals

nautilus shells

trees

These patterns are called

FRACTALS.

MEET FRACTAL!

Hi. I'm Fractal. You can call me Fractal.

If you zoom in on me you will see that I am a repeating pattern.
But (here comes the really great bit) the pattern gets smaller
and smaller as it repeats.

Hey – not too close. Mind my
personal fractal space!

I bet you wish you were
a repeating pattern.

TINY BRANCHES

Snowflakes are some of the
smallest fractals in nature.

Each snowflake has lots of tiny,
repeating branches of ice that grow
in different directions.

SNOWFLAKE SECRETS

The pattern of each snowflake is unique but all snowflakes have six-fold symmetry. This means you can spin them around six different ways and they still look identical.

YES: I knew you'd know what this means.

SNOWFLAKES ARE HEXAGONAL!

Remember me?
We met on page 48.

Circle all the hexagonal shapes here:

dice

door

honeycomb

stop sign

bank card

star

tortoise shell

clock

daffodil

SPOT THE SNOW FLAKE

One of these snowflakes is not like the others. Can you spot which one?

How to

MAKE A SNOWFLAKE

You will need

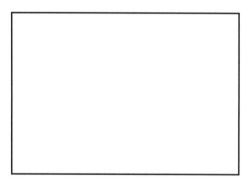

A sheet of A4 paper

A pair of scissors

1. Fold your paper.

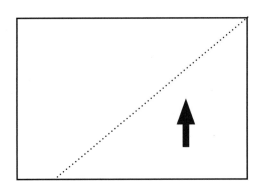 =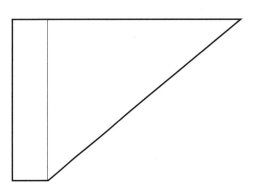

2. Cut the excess paper to make a perfect square.

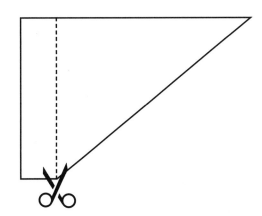 =

3. Fold the square into a triangle, and then a smaller triangle.

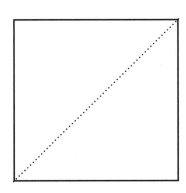 =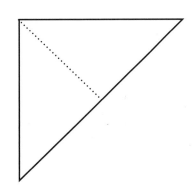

4. Fold the right corner of the triangle into two smaller triangles.

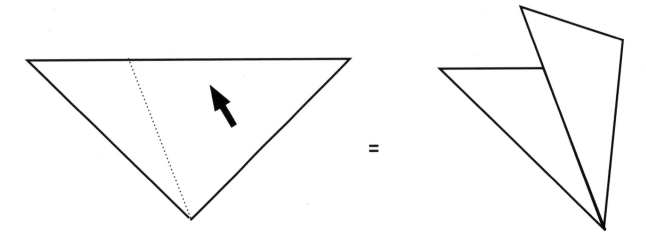

=

5. Repeat on the left side.

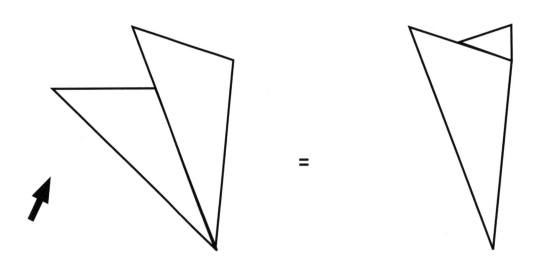

=

6. Cut along the top.

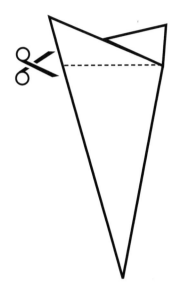 =

7. Cut again.

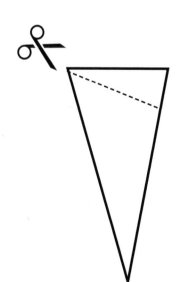 =

8. Cut the folded triangle in three spots, as marked.

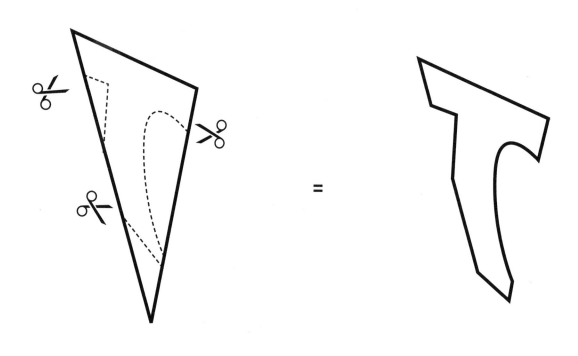

=

....

Hint: You can cut as many shapes as you like into the folded triangle to create a more detailed snowflake.

....

9. Unfold to reveal your snowflake.

KN❄W Y❄UR SN❄W

A snowflake is a crystal of snow.

The Eskimos have many types of snow so they have different words for them.

Here are a few of them:

aqilokoq	snow that falls softly
piegnartoq	snow that is good for driving a sled on
aputi	snow on the ground
muruaneq	soft deep snow
aniu	snow used to make water
siku	ice in general

How many words can you make out of the word SNOWFLAKE? P.S. There are 314, but **DON'T PANIC**. You don't need to find all of them.

Can you find 10 words?

MY 10 SNOWFLAKE WORDS:

1. _____

2. _____

3. _____

4. _____

5. _____

6. _____

7. _____

8. _____

9. _____

10. _____

COLDER AND COLDER

Find these cold words huddling together
in this word search:

arctic   chilly   frigid   glacial

polar   wintry   gelid   icy

```
K F D B G X T M J R U S H X B L
V L O S W C B G J X K N Z N A Y
A I M G T H F A B P L B B I I F
H L C Z A K R I Q N I S C G D P
V S A Y Y G I M J O R A R K U O
I E O C T O G U S C L Q Z W F L
A R C T I C I D U G D S X P J A
Y A W T J L D M V N K B L X C R
N G H C L U X P H G F O E Q M L
K V I J N A Z N E C D Z O E K J
U H X M B P W Q Y L Y K T O N K
D W E V O C J U L A D H H V Z Y
I B L F P E Z K L O R F O P N W
L I Q D S T D T I J Y X M D T E
E V I H C U Q O H W I N T R Y D
G S W U R Q I A C M G E Q U T S
```

GETTING WARMER

Find these hot words so you can thaw out:

boiling   scorching   sizzling   fiery
scalding   tropical   sweltry   humid

```
S  F  D  B  G  X  T  M  J  R  U  S  H  X  G  M
C  L  O  S  W  C  B  G  J  X  K  N  Z  N  F  Y
A  W  M  G  T  H  F  A  B  P  L  B  I  S  I  F
L  L  R  S  Z  K  R  I  Q  N  I  L  A  G  E  Y
D  S  A  C  C  G  I  M  J  O  Z  A  R  K  R  E
I  Z  Y  O  H  Q  W  E  R  Z  V  Q  Z  W  Y  W
N  L  Z  R  T  Z  C  D  I  P  D  S  X  P  S  I
G  A  W  C  Z  L  W  S  V  N  K  B  L  X  W  M
N  G  H  H  O  U  X  P  H  G  F  O  E  Q  E  L
K  V  I  I  V  A  Z  N  E  C  D  Z  O  E  L  J
U  H  X  N  H  P  W  D  C  L  Y  K  T  O  T  K
D  W  E  G  K  C  I  U  Q  A  D  H  H  V  R  Y
J  B  L  T  Q  M  Z  B  O  I  L  I  N  G  Y  G
T  I  Q  D  U  T  D  T  S  J  Y  X  M  D  T  E
Z  V  I  H  C  U  Q  O  N  B  U  H  P  I  Y  D
Q  T  R  O  P  I  C  A  L  M  G  E  Q  U  T  S
```

The FINGERPRINT GALLERY

Fingerprinting

Just as every single snowflake is unique,
your fingerprints are unique too.

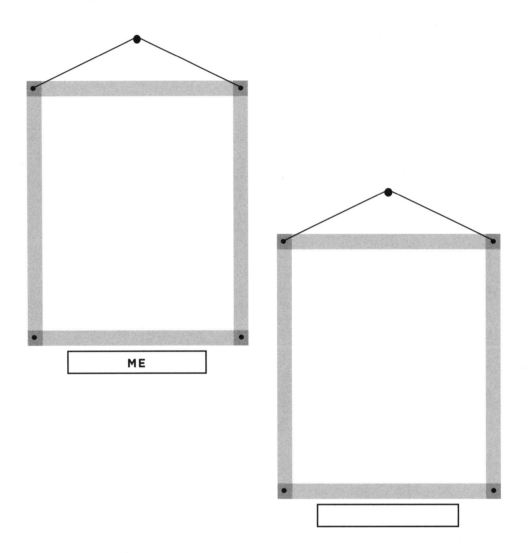

ME

A Collect your family's fingerprints. There might be
a mystery to solve in your house one day.

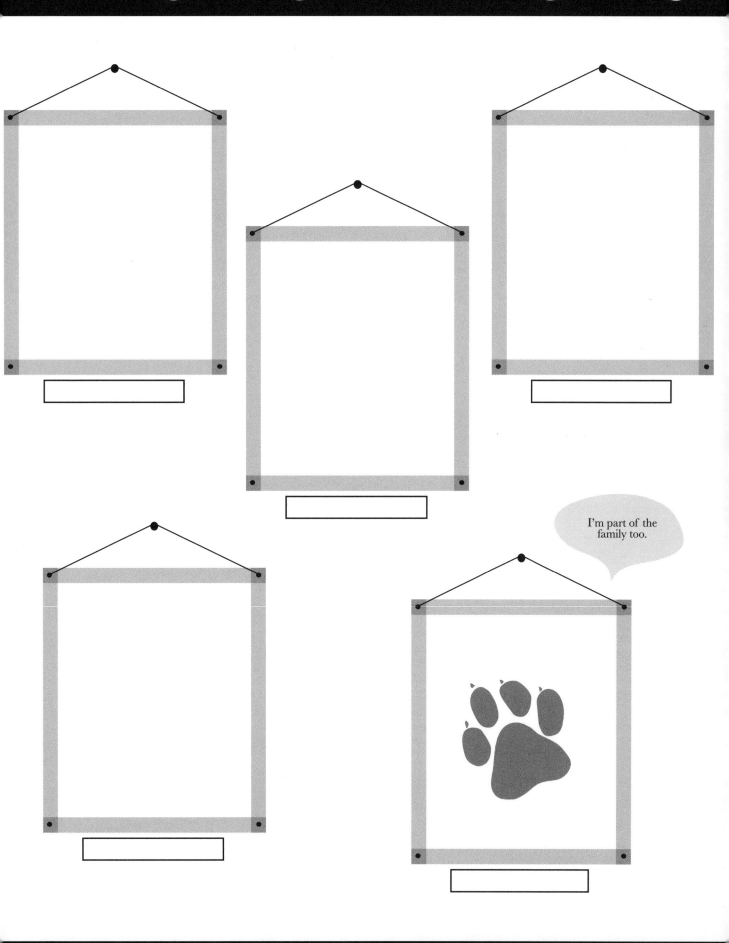

THE CASE OF THE MYSTERIOUS MYSTERY

WHAT CRIME HAS BEEN COMMITTED? _____

_____

_____

_____

_____

DESCRIBE THE CRIME SCENE: _____

_____

_____

_____

WHO ARE THE MAIN SUSPECTS ? (give them nicknames) _____

_____

_____

_____

THE CASE OF THE MYSTERIOUS MYSTERY

WHAT ARE THEIR ALIBIS? _____

_____

_____

_____

_____

CAN ANYONE ELSE CORROBORATE THEIR ALIBIS? _____

_____

_____

_____

_____

WHO DO YOU SUSPECT MOST AND WHY? _____

_____

_____

_____

_____

104

FINAL CRIME REPORT

YOUR CRIME CONCLUSION:

SUSPECT APPREHENDED:

OUTCOME:

TREE TALK TREE TREE

TREE TALK TREE TREE

TREE TALK TREE TREE

TREE TALK TREE TREE

TREE TALK TREE TREE

TREE TALK TREE TREE

One type of fractal design is called

branching.

The branches of trees grow out from
the trunk, becoming smaller and smaller
as they get further away from the trunk.

This kind of pattern allows oxygen and
carbon dioxide to flow through
the whole tree.

LOOKING AT LEAVES

Leaves have a similar kind of pattern.

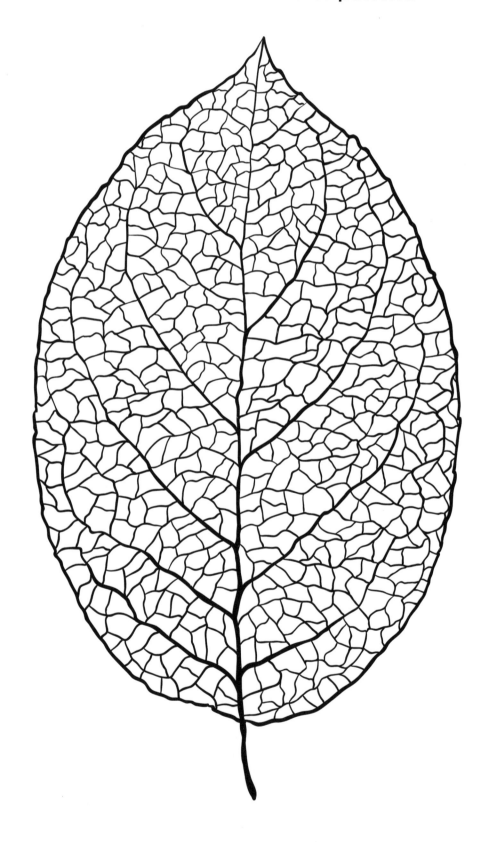

111

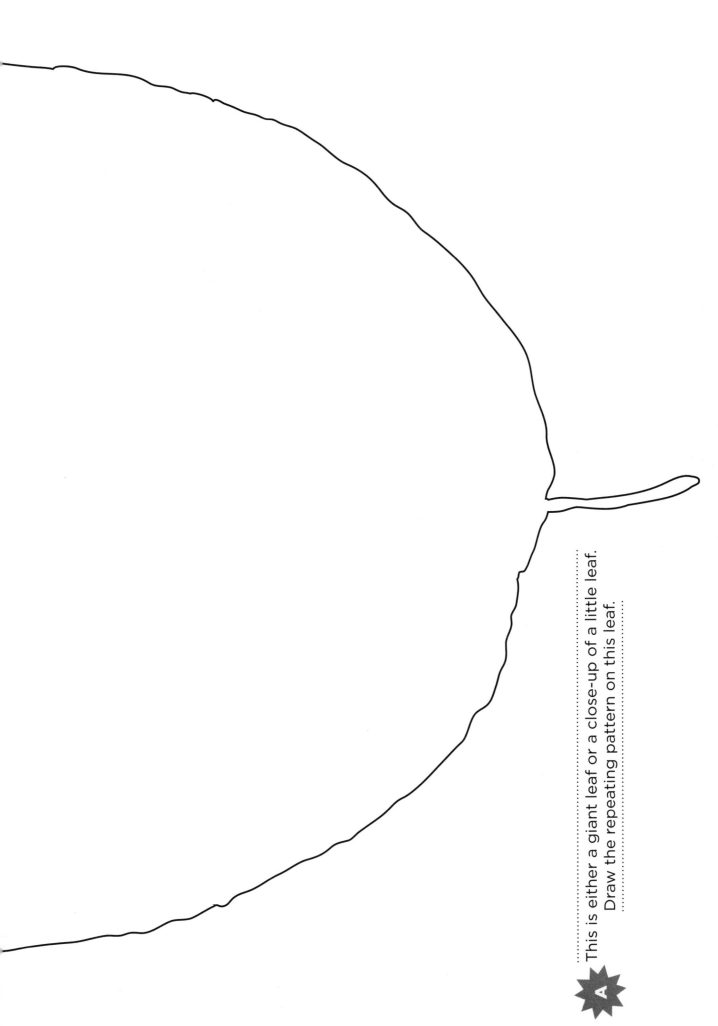

This is either a giant leaf or a close-up of a little leaf.
Draw the repeating pattern on this leaf.

The spiral is another type of fractal in nature.

A nautilus shell curves in a special spiral
called a **logarithmic spiral.**

FLASH FACT:
The bellybutton
nautilus is the smallest
nautilus of all.
It measures only
about 16 cm.

START HERE!

 Can you find your way through this spiral maze?

Galaxies are the biggest spirals in the universe.

GALAXY

Q: What do you call a hand with a trillion fingers?

A single spiral galaxy may have a trillion stars.

Too many stars to count on your fingers. Unless you have a trillion fingers.

QUEST

A trillion is a million million.

A: A handful.

STARRY, STARRY NIGHT

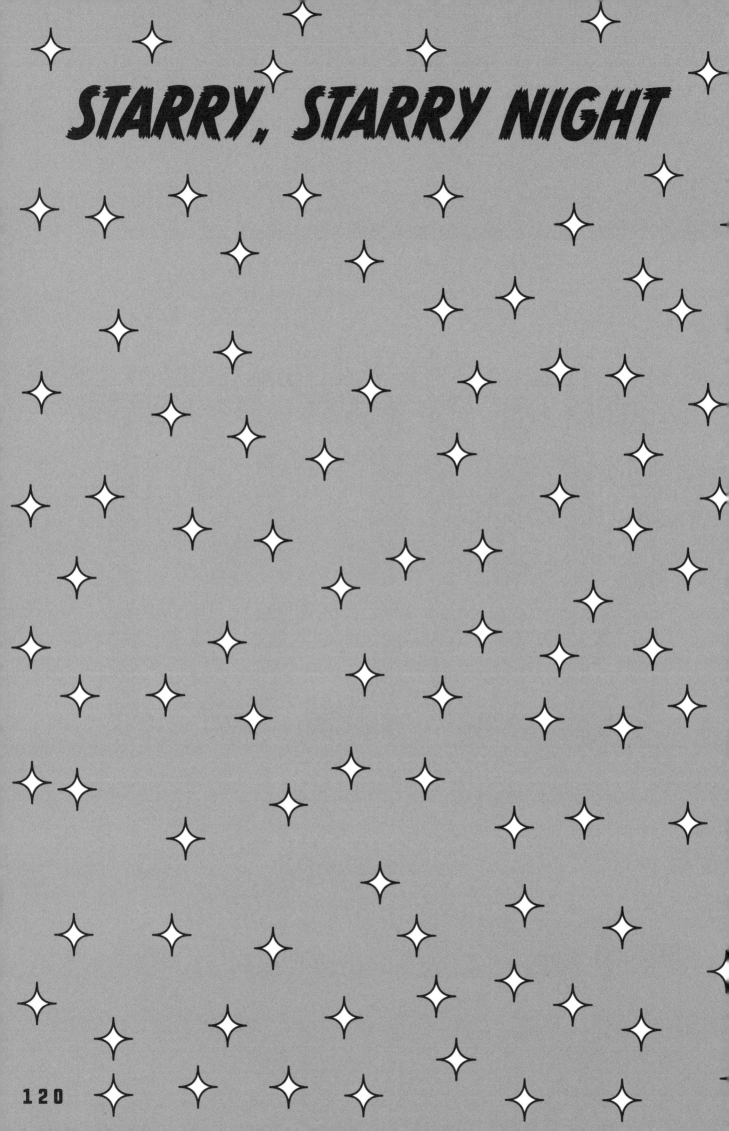

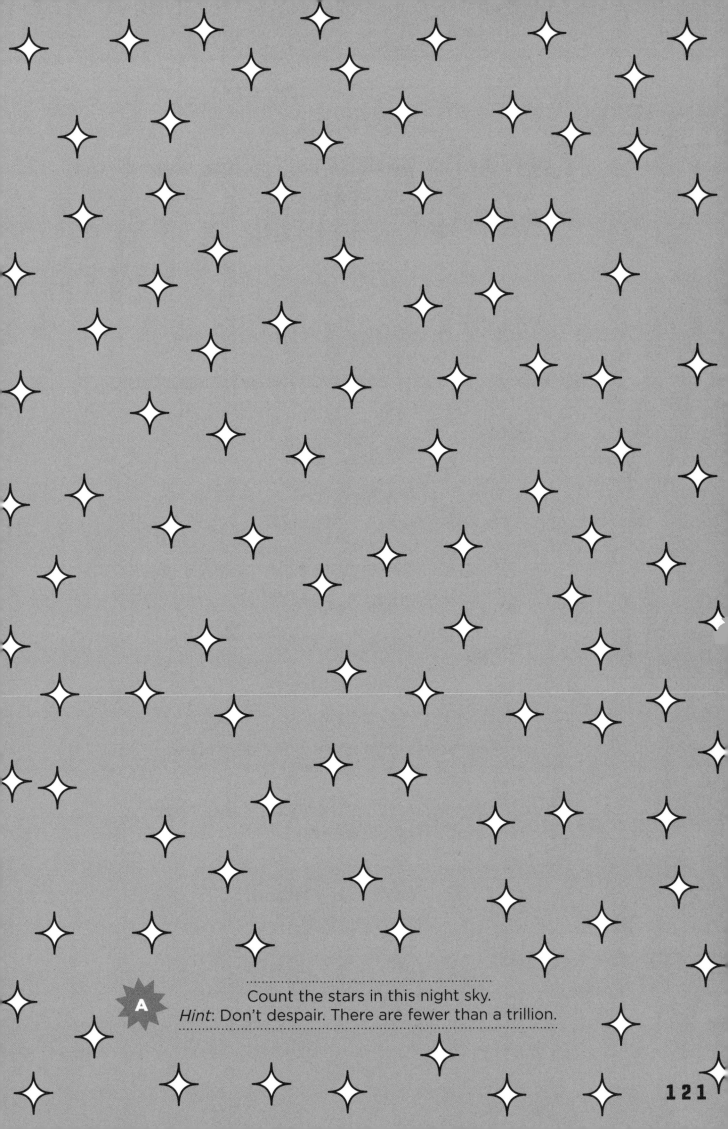

Count the stars in this night sky.
Hint: Don't despair. There are fewer than a trillion.

TWINKLE TWINKLE LITTLE STAR

If I asked you to draw a star, I bet you'd draw this:

This is how most people in the world draw stars.

Starfish look like this.

A gold star on your homework looks like this.

Stars on flags look like this.

BUT: there isn't a single star in the universe that is pointy.

Stars aren't star-shaped.

STARRY WORDS

There are more than 150 words that have **'*star*'** in them.

Can you think of twenty? Here's one to get your *star*-ted.

1. megastar *That's you!*

2. _____

3. _____

4. _____

5. _____

6. _____

7. _____

8. _____

9. _____

10. _____

11. _____

12. _____

13. _____

14. _____

15. _____

16. _____

17. _____

18. _____

19. _____

20. _____

STARS ARE HOT

The Sun is a large star. It is round – not pointy.

EARTH

SUN

The Earth is tiny next to a star. Stars burn with nuclear fires and, like everything in the universe, they will not last forever.

Many stars will go out with a **BANG**.

A Draw an exploding star. Make it *explosive*.

FLASH FACT: All of the gold in the world was made inside an exploding star.

GOLD STARS FOR YOU

You've earned a page of gold stars.
Colour them in.

THE UNIVERSE HAS SOME
REALLY BIG NUMBERS

 Make up your own alphabet of really big numbers.

I've put in the names of some existing really big numbers to help you get started. Be as inventive as you can. Make those numbers sound **LARGE.**

A _____

B bazillion

C centillion

D _____

E _____

F _____

G gazillion

H _____

I _____

J jillion

K _____

L _____

M _____

N _____

O _____

P _____

Q quadrillion

Hi. I'm Quad.
Remember me?
See page 72

R _____

S squillion

T trillion

U umptillion

V _____

W _____

X _____

Y _____

Z zillion

CoDe yOU

You have just created a unique alphabet
of Really Big Numbers.

Use this alphabet to write
secret codes to your friends.

Write a message and give it to a friend
(or two) to decode.

MY MESSAGE IN CODE

MY MESSAGE DECODED

CODE CIPHER

Another simple number code is called
the number cipher.

All you have to do is substitute a letter
for a number, for example:

A	B	C	D	E	F	G	H	I	J	K	L	M
1	2	3	4	5	6	7	8	9	10	11	12	13

N	O	P	Q	R	S	T	U	V	W	X	Y	Z
14	15	16	17	18	19	20	21	22	23	24	25	26

To make it trickier (and harder for someone else to crack), you could start with your age. So if you are 9, you would start **A** at **9** and so on.

 Using the cipher on page 132, here is a secret message from me for you to decode:

13　1　20　8　19

9　19

13　1　7　9　3

Your answer:

_____

CODE CRACKER

The international Morse Code uses dots and dashes for letters and numbers.

In the old days, they would send messages by a telegraph using Morse Code.

A	● ▬		N	▬ ●
B	▬ ● ● ●		O	▬ ▬ ▬
C	▬ ● ▬ ●		P	● ▬ ▬ ●
D	▬ ● ●		Q	▬ ▬ ● ▬
E	●		R	● ▬ ●
F	● ● ▬ ●		S	● ● ●
G	▬ ▬ ●		T	▬
H	● ● ● ●		U	● ● ▬
I	● ●		V	● ● ● ▬
J	● ▬ ▬ ▬		W	● ▬ ▬
K	▬ ● ▬		X	▬ ● ● ▬
L	● ▬ ● ●		Y	▬ ● ▬ ▬
M	▬ ▬		Z	▬ ▬ ● ●

Get ready to dot and dash, and solve
these Morse codes.

1. ●■   ●●● ■ ●● ■ ●■●■ ●●●●   ●● ■●   ■ ●● ■■ ●
●●● ●■ ●●●■ ● ●●●   ■● ●● ■● ●

_____

_____

2. ●●   ● ●■ ■   ■●■● ●●●● ■■■ ■●■● ■■■ ●■●● ●■ ■ ●
●●■● ■■■ ●■●   ■●●● ●■● ● ●■ ■●■ ●■●● ●■ ●●● ■

_____

_____

3. ■■ ●■ ■ ●●●● ●●●   ●● ●●●   ■■ ■●■■
●●■● ●■ ●●●■ ■■■ ●■ ●■● ●● ■ ●
●●● ●●■ ■●●● ●■■■ ● ■●■● ■ .

_____

_____

4. ■●●● ●■ ■●■● ■●■   ■ ■■■   ●●● ■●■● ●●■ ●■ ●■● ●
■■ ■● ● .

_____

_____

5. ●■ ●■● ●   ■●■● ■■■ ●●■   ●●● ■ ●● ●■●● ●■●●
●■● ● ●■ ■●● ●● ■● ■■   ■ ●●●● ●● ●●●
●■■● ●■ ■●● ● ?

_____

_____

A Make up some of your own messages in Morse Code and give them to a friend to decipher.

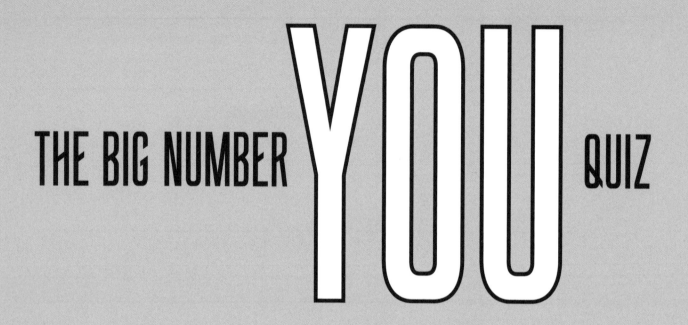

THE BIG NUMBER YOU QUIZ

WARNING: This quiz is not for the fainthearted. You are going to encounter some **MASSIVE** numbers.

Be **brave**.

Be **bold**.

How many seconds in an hour?

_____

How many hours in a day?

_____

How many seconds in a day?

_____

How many hours in a week?

_____

How many seconds in a week?

_____

How many hours in a 30-day month?

_____

How many seconds in a 30-day month?

_____

How many hours in a year?

_____

How old are you?

_____

How many hours have you been alive?

_____

NAME *THAT* GALAXY

There are billions and billions of galaxies in our universe.

They haven't all been named yet but some have.

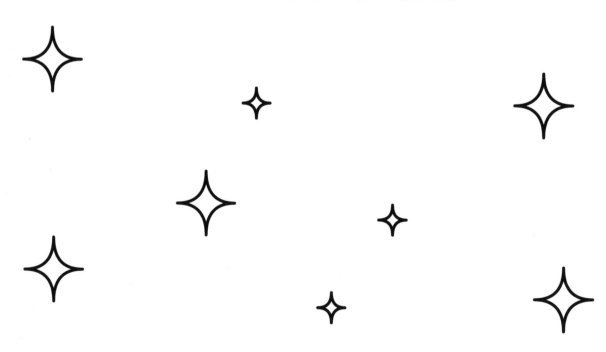

Some of these galaxies names are real, and some are not. Can you tell which are which?

Add a **T** next to the ones you think are True and an **F** next to the ones you think are False.

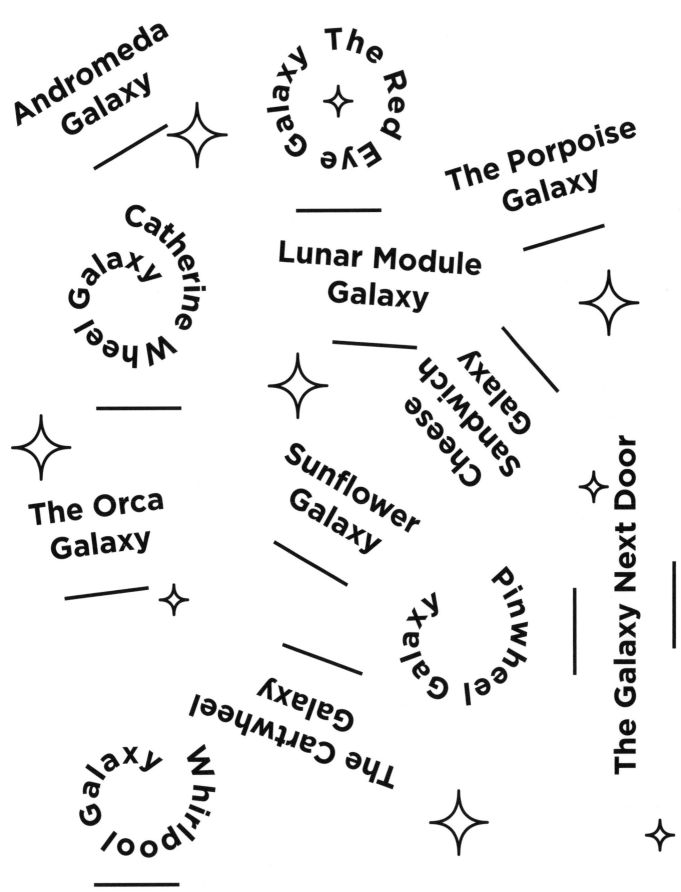

Andromeda Galaxy

The Red Eye Galaxy

The Porpoise Galaxy

Catherine Wheel Galaxy

Lunar Module Galaxy

Cheese Sandwich Galaxy

The Orca Galaxy

Sunflower Galaxy

Pinwheel Galaxy

The Galaxy Next Door

The Cartwheel Galaxy

Whirlpool Galaxy

Cyclones are the **largest spirals** on Earth.

CIRCLING IN

They form over warm oceans and have *ENORMOUS* power.

In some parts of the world, they are called hurricanes, or typhoons.

But if one is on the way,
don't hang around to find out
what it's called ...

N CYCLONES

RUN.

TAKE COVER.

CYCLONE WATCH

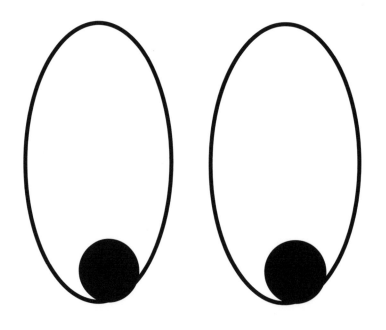

Cyclones used to be given female names. But now they are named after males *and* females.

Find out when and where these Australian cyclones occurred.

CYCLONE TRACY:

WHEN

WHERE

CYCLONE DEBBIE:

WHEN

WHERE

CYCLONE INGRID:

WHEN

WHERE

CYCLONE GEORGE:

WHEN

WHERE

A Think of some good names for cyclones. You may need them one day.

_____

_____

_____

_____

_____

_____

_____

_____

CHARGING
UP

A lightning bolt is also an example
of a fractal in nature.

Yep. I'm a natural.

It is a massive electrical charge that builds up
in a storm cloud because water droplets are *swirling*
fiercely around inside it.

When the cloud can't hold on to these droplets
any longer, they **burst** out from the cloud in a bolt of
lightning (a little like a pot of boiling water that overflows).

The bolt is in a hurry to reach the ground so it

twists and bends on the way down.

STRIKES

A Colour in this lightning pattern using vibrant fiery colours such as orange, red and yellow.

STORMY WEATHER

Lightning often forms in cumulonimbus clouds.
These are the clouds that look like giant cauliflowers,
rising high in the sky.

A Draw some vegetable clouds.

Kids LOVE vegetables!

REACHING FOR

Cumulonimbus are the highest, grandest clouds of all.
Clouds descend in this order:

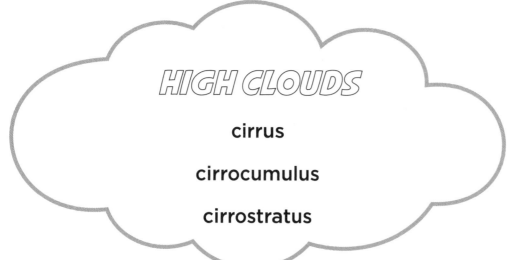

HIGH CLOUDS

cirrus

cirrocumulus

cirrostratus

MIDDLE CLOUDS

altocumulus

nimbostratus

altostratus

LOW CLOUDS

cumulus

stratus

stratocumulus

THE CLOUDS

What kind of cloud would you like to be?

Keep a cloud diary for a week.
Name and draw the clouds you see each day.

CLOUD WEEK

Date started: _____

DAY ONE:

FLASH FACT:
The study of clouds is called nephology.

DAY TWO:

157

DAY THREE:

DAY FOUR:

DAY FIVE:

DAY SIX:

DAY SEVEN:

THE
INSIDE

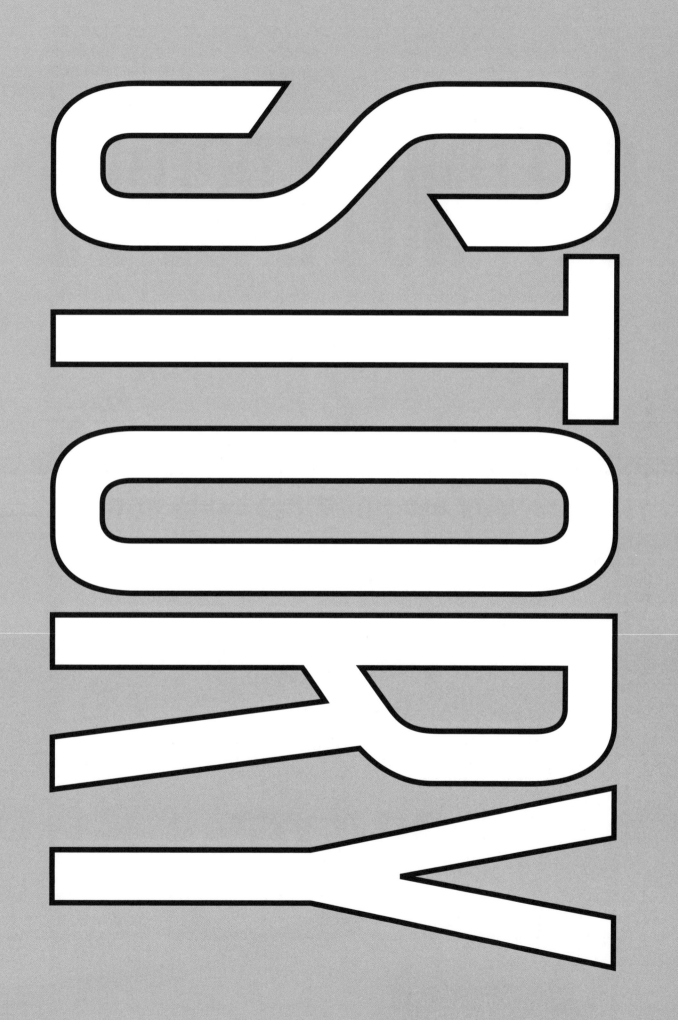

GETTING PERSONAL

Maths is EVERYWHERE: even inside us.

Q: Why are lightning bolts and blood vessels similar?

Is this a joke? It's not very funny.

A: Because they have the same shape.

Well, this answer is unexpected.

OR IS IT?

MATHS FINDS CONNECTIONS BETWEEN THINGS THAT SEEM COMPLETELY DIFFERENT

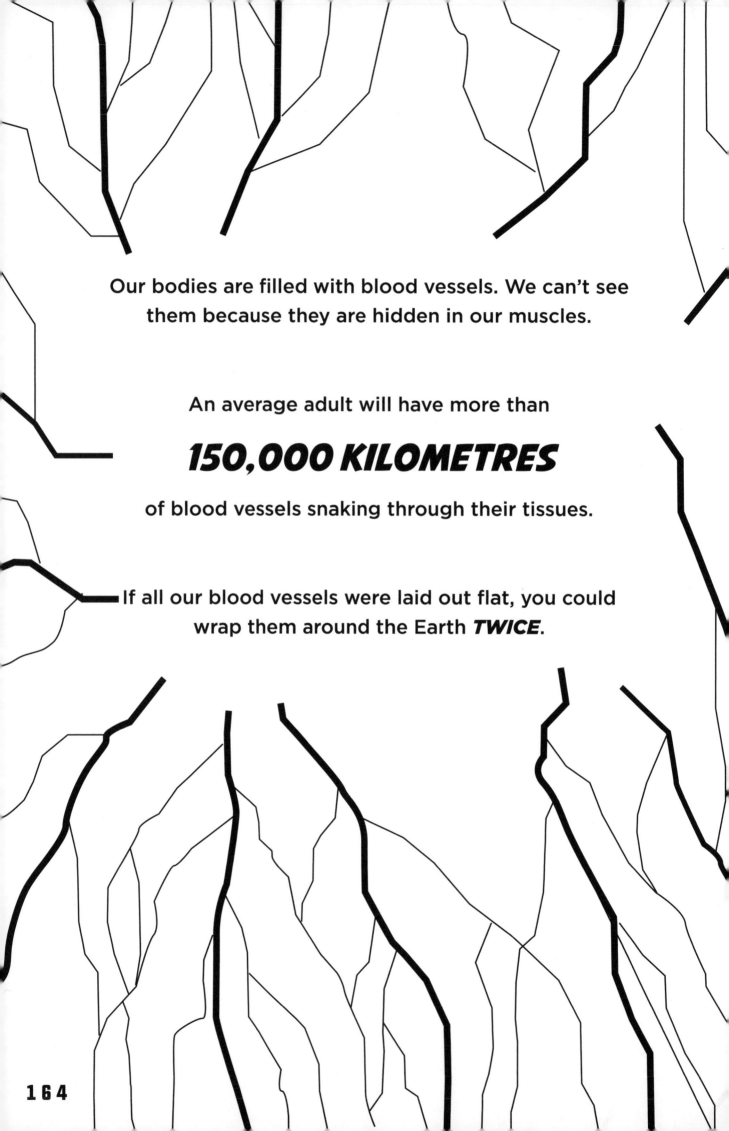

Our bodies are filled with blood vessels. We can't see them because they are hidden in our muscles.

An average adult will have more than

150,000 KILOMETRES

of blood vessels snaking through their tissues.

If all our blood vessels were laid out flat, you could wrap them around the Earth *TWICE*.

BIG BODY

Our body is made up of some spectacular numbers.

A Match the description with the right part of the body.

We are born with **350** of these but by the time we become an adult we only have **206**.   brain

                                                                                                                eye

We take approx. **20,000** of these each day.

                                                                                                                sneezes

We have more than **37 trillion** in our body.

                                                                                                                tongue

These can travel at speeds of up to **160 km/hr.**

                                                                                                                bones

This has around **3 million** sweat glands.

                                                                                                                small intestine

This beats up to about **35 million** times a year.

                                                                                                                breaths

This contains more than **120 million** light-sensitive cells.

                                                                                                                cells

This has between **3000-10,000** taste buds.

                                                                                                                skin

This weighs around **1.5 kg.**

                                                                                                                heart

This is up to **4 times** the height of an adult.

The *heart* of the matter

Blood vessels need to supply blood to every cell in the body.

BVs RULE!

Like the leaves on a tree and bolts of lightning, they stretch and grow and have the most efficient pattern possible to reach every centimetre of muscle and organ.

As we get bigger and bigger, these blood vessels expand seamlessly too.

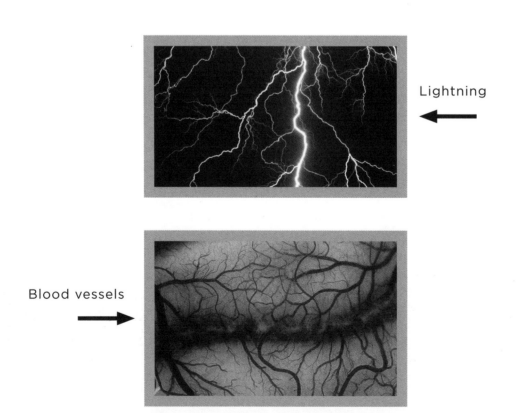

Lightning ←

Blood vessels →

Quizzing you on fractals

1. Fractals are:
  a) broken limbs
  b) misspelt facts
  c) never-ending patterns.

2. Fractals can be found:
  a) inside a jam jar
  b) everywhere
  c) at the bottom of the sea.

3. An average adult has how many blood vessels inside them?
  a) a trillion
  b) a lot
  c) 150,000 kilometres.

4. A lightning bolt is:
  a) in a hurry to get to the ground
  b) late for a date with a storm cloud
  c) a new kind of soft drink.

5. Which is the odd one out in this list?
  sunflower, nautilus shell, cumulonimbus, galaxy, snowflake.

TIED UP IN KNOTS

There are some truly extraordinary things
going on in your body.
Each cell in your body is full of knots that
make you who you are.

It's time to meet:

DEOXYRIBONUCLEIC ACID.

DNA for short.

DNA is an acronym.

WHAT ACRONYM IS THAT?

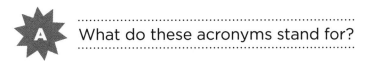

A What do these acronyms stand for?

RADAR

_____

SCUBA

_____

POSH

_____

LOL

_____

RSVP

_____

AC

_____

ATM

_____

BLT

_____

ET

_____

ROYGBIV

_____

DNA sounds impressive because it is. It carries the genetic instructions that govern the growth and functioning of all known organisms. It is essentially a code for organic molecules that are strung together in a very specific order.

Our genetic code is really long so it can carry all the information required to make you **YOU** (and me **ME**).

If you took the DNA from just a single cell in your body and stretched it all the way out, it would be about 2 metres long.

2m ▬▬▬ **DNA**

1.75m ▬

1.5m ▬▬▬

1.25m ▬▬

1m ▬▬▬

0.75m ▬▬

0.5m ▬▬

0.25m ▬▬

HOW TALL ARE YOU?

A Mark your height and the height of your friends and family on this chart.

DNA RULES

There are about **37 trillion** cells in an average human body. If you lined up the total amount of DNA in your body, it would be more than **74,000,000,000,000** kilometres long – from end to end. That's about the same as taking a round trip from here to the Sun – **250 times!**

BUT: it's stored in a space smaller than the human eye can see?

Q: **How can that be?**

A: **Your DNA is coiled up in knots.**

THINGS GET KNOTTY

Mathematical knots are different from the knots you tie in your shoelaces.

The most basic kind of knot in your body is one that, really, isn't knotted at all.

The technical name for this is the *'unknot'*. It <u>never</u> crosses or loops back over itself.

Even as you read this, your cells are tying and untying knots to keep you alive.

A: Knot funny.

I love a good magic trick.

Here's one for you.

You will need

A full deck of cards

without the jokers

But we're the funny ones!

1. Shuffle the cards.

2. Divide the deck into four piles according to the following steps:

   a) Uncover the first card in the deck. If it is red, place it face-up on your left. If it is black, place it face-up on your right.

   b) After you have placed the first card, take the second card – which you have not uncovered or looked at – and place it in its own pile above the first card. You now have your first two piles: an uncovered pile and a secret pile.

   c) Uncover the third card, and treat it just like the first card – place it face-up on your right or left in the appropriate red or black pile.

   d) Take the fourth card and treat it just like the second card – without looking at it, place it face-down in its own pile above the third card.

   e) Repeat this process until you've gone through the entire deck.

   If you've been following so far, you should have four piles of cards in front of you: a red uncovered pile, a black uncovered pile, and two secret piles – one for each colour.

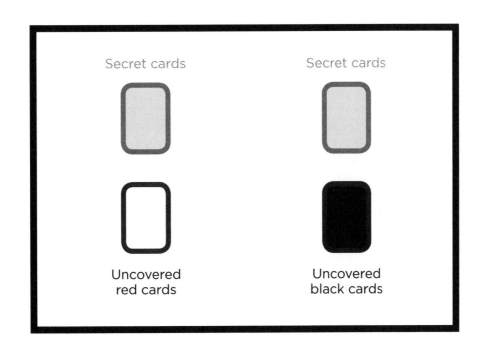

3. Enlist the help of a friend.

4. Tell her or him to select a random number between **1** and **6**.

5. If they select, for example, 5, ask them to take out any 5 cards from one of the secret piles.

6. Without looking at any of the cards, swap those 5 cards with any 5 cards from the other secret pile.

   Now the secret piles have been jumbled up with each other and there's no way you could know anything at all about the contents of the secret cards.

HERE COMES THE TRICK.

7. Announce grandly to your audience that you will now make a magical prediction.

   You predict that the number of red cards in the secret pile on the left is the same as the number of black cards in the secret pile on the right.

   And ... it is.

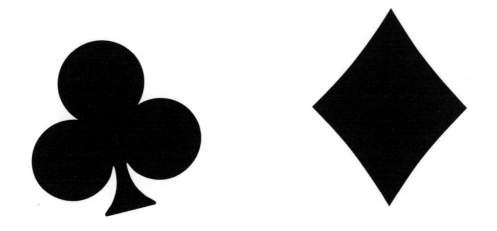

IT'S MAGIC!

Why is a rainbow round?

RAIN

BOW

Because it is made up of round raindrops.

⭐ **A** Count the raindrops on this page.

I AM A RAINBOW.

COLOUR ME.

PERFECT

PATTERNS

Maths helps us see patterns that are right in front of our noses.

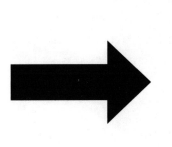

THE ANSWERS

TOP SECRET

THE ANSWERS

16

8

45

76

47

Odd numbers are numbers that can't be split into two equal groups of whole numbers.

77

83

31

56

82

34

2

99

12

74

73

44

1

84

51

HOW

60

57

3

5

38

85

37

81

7

13

33

25

68

66

48

40

4

79

55

6

20

94

26

30

95

9

75

43

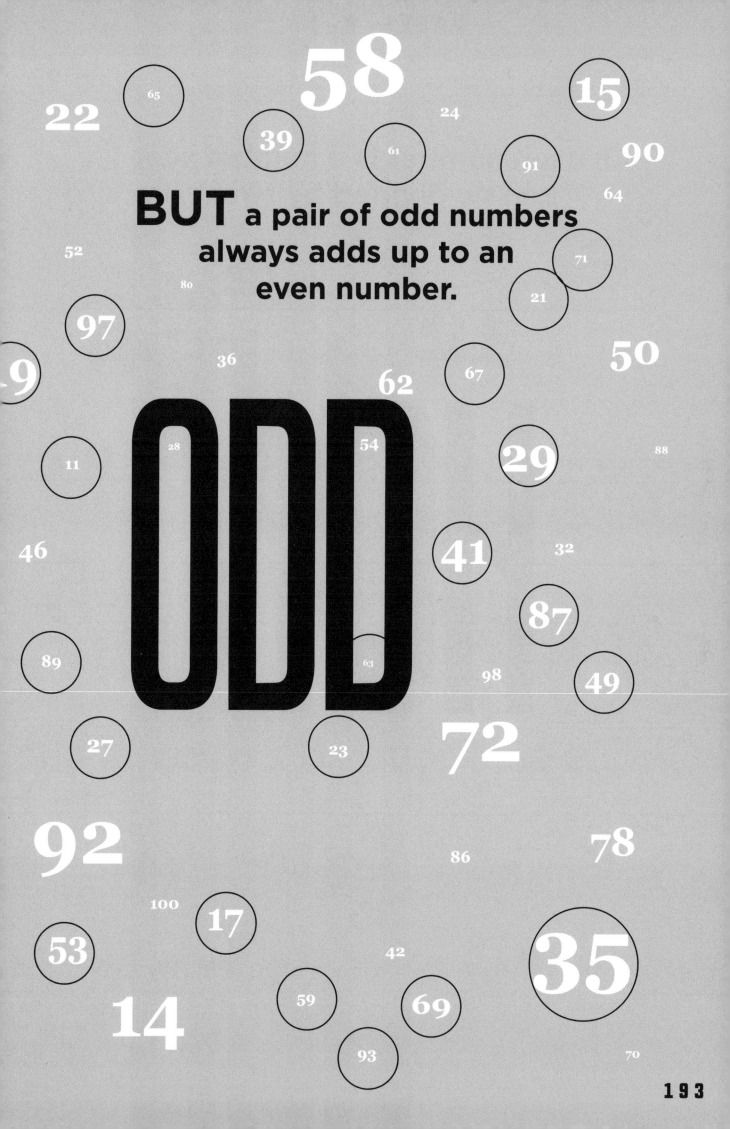

BUT a pair of odd numbers always adds up to an even number.

ODD

An even number is a number that can be divided by two.

58 65 22 15 24 39 61 90 91 64 52 71 80 21 97 9 36 96 50 67 62 29 88 28 54 11 32 41 46 87 98 63 49 89 27 23 72 92 86 78 100 17 53 42 35 14 59 69 93 70

EVEN

PAGE 8   ODDS GET EVEN

$1 + 3 = 4$

$3 + 5 = 8$

$5 + 7 = 12$

$7 + 9 = 16$

$9 + 11 = 20$

$11 + 13 = 24$

$13 + 15 = 28$

$15 + 17 = 32$

$17 + 19 = 36$

$19 + 21 = 40$

$21 + 23 = 44$

$23 + 25 = 48$

$25 + 27 = 52$

$27 + 29 = 56$

PAGE 13   TRUE OR FALSE

2 is one of my favourite numbers because:

	TRUE	FALSE
1. It's **1** more than **1**?	☒	☐
2. It rhymes with **WOO**?	☒	☐
3. **EDDIE** has **2** syllables?	☒	☐
4. I have **2** feet.	☒	☐
5. It takes me **2** minutes to eat a bar of chocolate.	☒	☐
6. Double trouble means **TROUBLE** x **2**.	☒	☐

PAGES 14-15   A TANGLE OF TWOS

There are 318 twos.

PAGE 43 SCRAMBLED CIRCLES

pies

pancakes

doughnuts

pizzas

meatballs

sushi

burgers

scones

cupcakes

Circle of friends

Circle of life

Vicious circles

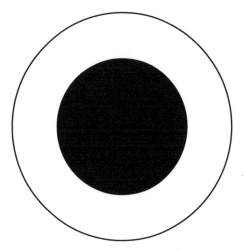

Inner circle

Winner's circle

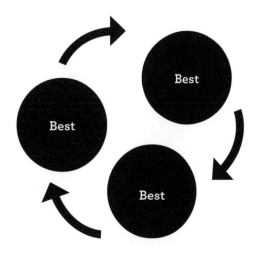

Move in the best circles

PAGES 52-53　A SPELLING BEE

EASY PEASY WORDS

I rhyme with bone and I ring. I am a **PHONE.**

I start with 't' and am not today or yesterday.
I am **TOMORROW.**

I have hands but I can't clap with them. I am a **CLOCK.**

LESS EASY WORDS

UNSCRAMBLE ME

fragile

contribution

fortune

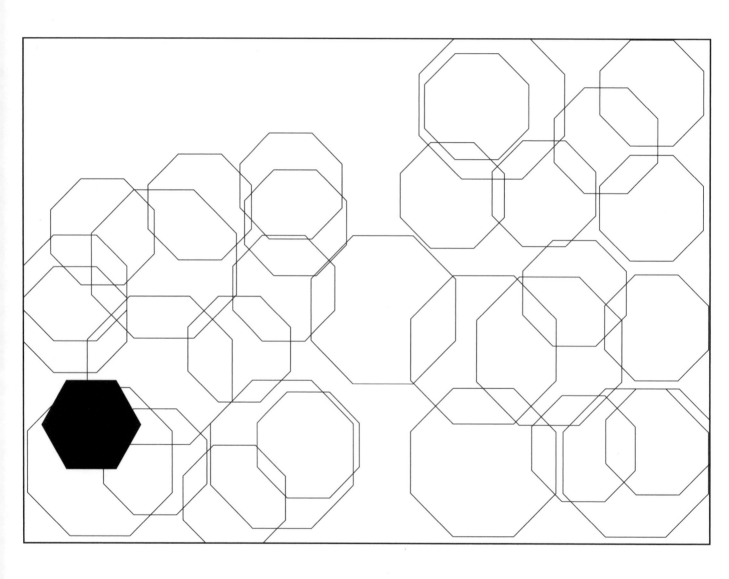

PAGE 58   OCTO SEARCH

```
K  F  D  B  G  X  T  M  J  R  U  S  H  X  B  M
V  L  O  S  W  C  B  G  J  X  K  N  O  N  P  Y
A  W  M  G  T  H  F  A  B  P  L  B  C  S  I  F
H  L  R  Z  A  K  R  I  Q  N  I  S  T  G  D  Y
V  S  A  R  Y  G  I  M  J  O  R  A  O  K  U  E
I  E  O  C  T  O  P  U  S  C  V  Q  N  W  F  W
W  L  Z  R  Z  C  D  U  P  D  S  A  P  J  I
Y  A  W  T  J  L  W  M  V  N  K  B  U  X  C  M
N  G  H  C  L  U  X  P  H  G  F  O  T  Q  M  L
K  V  I  J  N  A  Z  R  E  C  D  Z  S  E  K  R
U  H  X  M  B  P  O  Q  C  L  Y  K  T  O  N  E
D  W  E  V  O  T  J  U  Q  A  D  H  H  V  Z  B
J  B  L  F  C  E  Z  K  Y  O  R  F  O  P  N  O
T  I  Q  O  S  T  D  T  S  J  Y  X  M  D  T  T
Z  V  D  H  C  U  Q  O  N  B  U  H  P  I  Y  C
Q  S  O  C  T  O  G  E  N  E  R  I  A  N  T  O
```

PAGES 60-61   A SHOCK OF SPIDERS

104 spiders × 8 legs = 832 spiders' legs

TRIANGLE

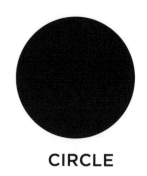

CIRCLE

SQUARE

RECTANGLE

PENTAGON

HEXAGON

OCTAGON

TRAPEZIUM

quadrangle ⋯⋯⋯⋯⋯⋯⋯ four siblings

quadrillion ⋯⋯⋯⋯⋯⋯⋯ a square or rectangular space
surrounded by buildings

quadruped ⋯⋯⋯⋯⋯⋯⋯ a really **large** number

quadruplets ⋯⋯⋯⋯⋯⋯⋯ walks on **four** feet

quadrille ⋯⋯⋯⋯⋯⋯⋯ a square dance performed by four couples

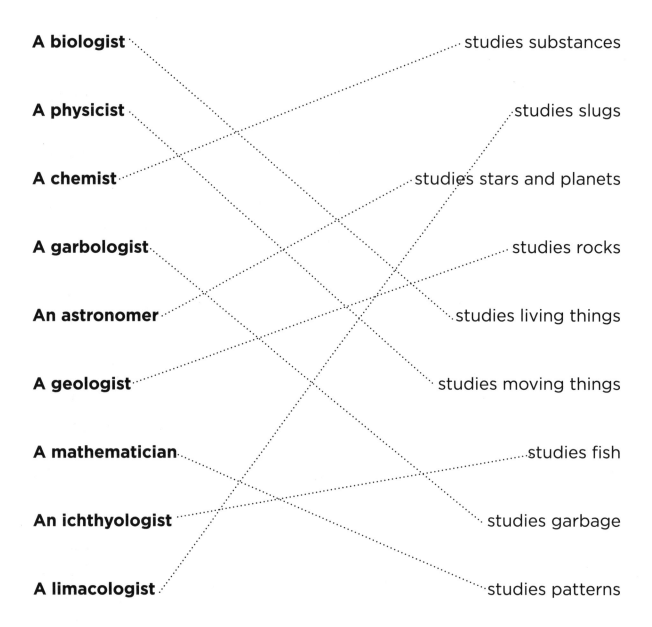

A biologist   studies substances

A physicist   studies slugs

A chemist   studies stars and planets

A garbologist   studies rocks

An astronomer   studies living things

A geologist   studies moving things

A mathematician   studies fish

An ichthyologist   studies garbage

A limacologist   studies patterns

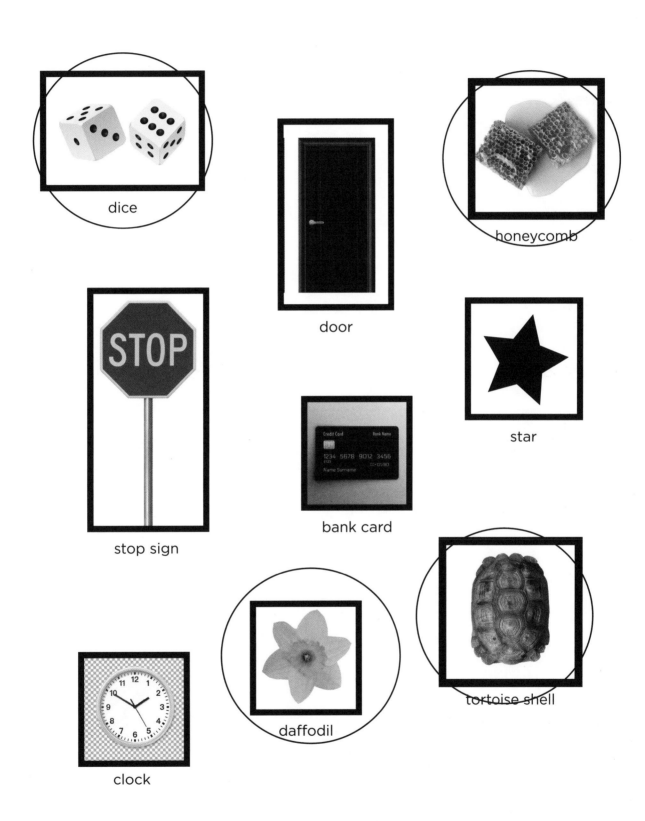

dice

door

honeycomb

stop sign

bank card

star

clock

daffodil

tortoise shell

SPOT
THE
SNOW
FLAKE

Ten words I made from 'snowflake' are:

ankle(s)

waken(s)

flake(s)

snake(s)

flown

lawn(s)

loaf

know(s)

askew

snow

PAGES 98-99

COLDER AND COLDER

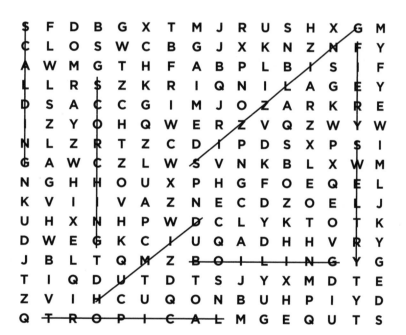

GETTING WARMER

PAGE 116 SPIRAL MAZE

PAGES 120-121 STARRY, STARRY NIGHT

There are 197 stars

Twenty 'star' words I thought of are:

starfish

starve

starving

startle

starburst

stargaze

superstar

starstruck

kickstart

upstart

starling

stardom

custard YUM!

mustard HOT!

start

starch

starry

stark

stardust

outstare

PAGE 133   CODE CIPHER

Maths

is

magic

PAGES 134-135   CODE CRACKER

1. A stitch in time saves nine.

2. I eat chocolate for breakfast.

3. Maths is my favourite subject.

4. Back to square one.

5. Are you still reading this page?

How many seconds in an hour?   3600

How many hours in a day?   24

How many seconds in a day?   86,400

How many hours in a week?   168

How many seconds in a week?   604,800

How many hours in a 30-day month?   720

How many seconds in a 30-day month? 2,592,000

How many hours in a year?   8760

How old are you?

How many hours have you been alive?

Andromeda Galaxy	**T**
Lunar Module Galaxy	**F**
Pinwheel Galaxy	**T**
Sunflower Galaxy	**T**
Catherine Wheel Galaxy	**F**
Cheese Sandwich Galaxy	**F**
Whirlpool Galaxy	**T**
The Cartwheel Galaxy	**T**
The Orca Galaxy	**F**
The Red Eye Galaxy	**F**
The Porpoise Galaxy	**T**
The Galaxy Next Door	**F**

CYCLONE TRACY:

WHEN   **1974**

WHERE   **DARWIN**

CYCLONE DEBBIE:

WHEN   **2017**

WHERE   **QUEENSLAND**

CYCLONE INGRID:

WHEN   **2005**

WHERE   **NORTHERN AUSTRALIA**

CYCLONE GEORGE:

WHEN   **2007**

WHERE   **WESTERN AUSTRALIA**

We are born with **350** of these but by the time we become an adult we only have **206**.

We take approx. **20,000** of these each day.

We have more than **37 trillion** in our body.

These can travel at speeds of up to **160 km/hr.**

This has around **3 million** sweat glands.

This beats up to about **35 million** times a year.

This contains more than **120 million** light-sensitive cells.

This has between **3000-10,000** taste buds.

This weighs around **1.5 kg.**

This is up to **4 times** the height of an adult.

brain

eye

sneezes

tongue

bones

small intestine

breaths

cells

skin

heart

1. Fractals are:
a) broken limbs
b) misspelt facts
c) never-ending patterns.

2. Fractals can be found:
a) inside a jam jar
b) everywhere
c) at the bottom of the sea.

3. An average adult has how many blood vessels inside them?
a) a trillion
b) a lot
c) 150,000 kilometres.

Trick question and trick answer. If you got both these answers, you are a genius. If you didn't, don't worry. You'll catch the trick next time.

4. A lightning bolt is:
a) in a hurry to get to the ground
b) late for a date with a storm cloud
c) a new kind of soft drink.

5. Which is the odd one out in this list?
sunflower, nautilus shell, **cumulonimbus**, galaxy, snowflake.

RADAR
Radio Detecting and Ranging

SCUBA
Self-contained Underwater Breathing Apparatus

POSH
Port Out Starboard Home

LOL
Laughing Out Loud

RSVP
répondez s'il vous plait

It's French

AC
Air Conditioning

ATM
Automated Teller Machine

YUM!

BLT
Bacon, Lettuce, Tomato

ET
Extra Terrestrial

EEK!

ROYGBIV
Red, Orange, Yellow, Green, Blue, Indigo, Violet

the colours of the rainbow

There are 86 raindrops.

THE

END